Book A

Specific Skill Series

Detecting the Sequence

Richard A. Boning

Fifth Edition

D1238443

SRA/McGraw-Hill

Columbus, Ohio

Cover, Back Cover, Wayne Lynch/Masterfile

SRA/McGraw-Hill

*A Division of The **McGraw·Hill** Companies*

Printed in the United States of America.

Send all inquiries to:
    SRA/McGraw-Hill
    250 Old Wilson Bridge Road, Suite 310
    Worthington, OH 43085

ISBN 0-02-687991-3

    5 6 7 8 9 IMP 00 99

To the Teacher

PURPOSE:

DETECTING THE SEQUENCE helps develop the important ability to determine time relationships—the order in which things happen. Proficiency in this often taken-for-granted skill is necessary in all kinds of academic and nonacademic reading, from narration to process explanation.

FOR WHOM:

The skill of DETECTING THE SEQUENCE is developed through a series of books spanning ten levels (Picture, Preparatory, A, B, C, D, E, F, G, H). The Picture Level is for pupils who have not acquired a basic sight vocabulary. The Preparatory Level is for pupils who have a basic sight vocabulary but are not yet ready for the first-grade-level book. Books A through H are appropriate for pupils who can read on levels one through eight, respectively. **The use of the *Specific Skill Series Placement Test* is recommended to determine the appropriate level.**

THE NEW EDITION:

DETECTING THE SEQUENCE has been designed to help improve students' skills in identifying the sequence of events within a reading selection. In this series, the variety of questions helps develop students' understanding of multiple ways of expressing time relationships. Questions are text-dependent rather than picture-dependent.

SESSIONS:

Short practice sessions are the most effective. It is desirable to have a practice session every day or every other day, using a few units each session.

To the Teacher

SCORING:

Pupils should record their answers on the reproducible worksheets. The worksheets make scoring easier and provide uniform records of the pupils' work. Using worksheets also avoids consuming the exercise books.

It is important for pupils to know how well they are doing. For this reason, units should be scored as soon as they have been completed. Then a discussion can be held in which pupils justify their choices. (The Integrated Language Activities, many of which are open-ended, do not lend themselves to an objective score; thus there are no answer keys for these pages.)

GENERAL INFORMATION ON *DETECTING THE SEQUENCE*:

DETECTING THE SEQUENCE helps develop sequence skills through three general types of questions: (1) those that focus directly on when an event happened; (2) those that focus on which of several events happened first (or last) among the events mentioned; and (3) those that focus on whether a particular event happened before, at the same time as, or after another. The teacher should make clear to students that a question reading "Which happened first (last)?" means "Which happened before (after) any of the *other answer choices*?" (not "Which happened first [last] in the entire reading selection?").

Answering questions in DETECTING THE SEQUENCE involves more than just reading for facts. Most questions require pupils to establish the time relationships between two separately stated ideas by utilizing time clues in the text. (On the Picture Level, pupils examine two pictures illustrating a sequence of events, and determine which event happened first.)

SUGGESTED STEPS:

On all levels above Picture, pupils should read each story carefully. At the end of each statement they should try to form a picture in their minds so that they will clearly understand what happened first, second, and so forth. As they read, pupils should look for key words that serve as sequence clues, such as *then*, *before*, *soon*, *finally*, *later*, *while*, *when*, and *now*. After finishing the story, pupils should review it mentally. Without looking at the story, they should be able to recall the sequence in which events occurred. If they cannot do this, they should reread the story. Pupils should then answer the questions on their worksheets. In answering, pupils may look at the story as often as necessary.

RELATED MATERIALS:

Specific Skill Series Placement Tests, which enable the teacher to place pupils at their appropriate levels in each skill, are available for the Elementary (Pre-1–6) and Midway (4–8) grade levels.

About This Book

In real life, things happen in a certain order. First one thing happens, then another. When you read a story, it is usually told in order, too. Things that happened first are told first. This story tells things in order.

> Jan ate her breakfast. Then she looked outside. She saw snow on the ground.

Sometimes the order is turned around, as in this sentence:

> Before Jan went out, she put on her hat.

Which happened first: *Jan went out* or *Jan put on her hat*? You can tell that Jan put on her hat first. The word *before* tells you. Words like *after*, *before*, *then*, *first*, and *last* are all clues. They let you know the order in which things happened.

Often one thing must happen before another thing can happen. You must get on your bike before you can ride it. You can't read a book until after you have opened it. You know what happens first because it would not make sense for things to happen the other way around.

In this book, you will read short stories. As you read, think about the order of the things that happen. Then read the question, "What happened first?" Read the sentences under it. Choose the sentence that tells what happened first.

Sam asked Pat to play ball. Sam and all his friends were waiting for her. Pat was a good player. First, she got her bat. Then Pat hit the ball far out on the grass. But everyone stayed in one place. Even Pat didn't move. Her bat had broken in two. Now there were two small bats on the grass.

What happened first?

A. Pat got her bat.

B. Pat's bat broke in two.

C. Sam asked Pat to play ball.

Pam's teacher wanted to see who could read the most books. Pam took out a lot of books. She did not watch TV. She did not go outside to play. Pam read ten books in one week. Do you think Pam read the most books?

What happened first?

A. Pam took out a lot of books.

B. Pam read ten books.

C. Pam did not watch TV.

Rosa got some seeds. Where could she plant them? There was no place outside. Then she had a plan. First, she put the seeds in big pots. Next, she gave them water. Soon leaves and flowers began to grow. Then Rosa was very happy.

What happened first?

A. Rosa had a plan.

B. Rosa got some seeds.

C. Rosa put seeds in pots.

Mr. Kim went for his walk in the park. It was his birthday. He was 75 today. Joe met him in the park and asked him over to his house. Joe opened the door. There was Mrs. Kim with a big birthday cake! There were all of Mr. Kim's friends! Mr. Kim was so happy. He laughed and thanked everyone.

What happened first?

A. Mr. Kim laughed and thanked everyone.

B. Joe met Mr. Kim in the park.

C. Mr. Kim went for a walk.

Viv and her big brother Jess went fishing. They wanted fish to cook. Viv and Jess went by the water. Then they fished for a while. Soon Viv could feel something at the end of her line. It was not a fish. It was an old shoe! Viv and Jess did not have fish for dinner.

14

What happened first?

A. Viv could feel something on her line.

B. Viv and Jess went fishing.

C. Viv and Jess had dinner.

When Jack turned 13, he went on a train without his mother or father. The people on the train were friendly. He talked to them. Then he gave his seat to a man who had some big bags. Jack came to his stop. He helped a woman off the train. Jack felt very good. He had helped two people. He told his dad, "I had the best time on my trip."

What happened first?

A. Jack talked to the people.

B. Jack gave up his seat.

C. Jack helped a woman.

A. Exercising Your Skill

Think about these sentences.

> I open the door **before** I go into the house.
> I close the door **after** I am inside.

Number your paper from 1 to 5. For each sentence, write **before** or **after**.

1. The sun comes up _____ I go to school.
2. The clouds roll in _____ it rains.
3. The ground is wet _____ it rains.
4. Sunday comes just _____ Monday.
5. It gets dark _____ the sun goes down.

B. Expanding Your Skill

Join a group of two other students. Then play "Before and After." The first student begins a sentence. The second one says something that comes **before**. The third one says something that comes **after**. (Like this: "I brush my teeth...**before** I go to bed...and **after** I eat breakfast.") Take turns beginning the sentence.

C. Exploring Language

There are four words next to each number. The words are not in the right order. On your paper, write the words in 1-2-3 order.

1. summer   fall   spring   winter

2. Wednesday   Monday   Saturday   Sunday

3. noon   night   morning   midnight

4. daytime   sunup   night   sundown

D. Expressing Yourself

Do one of these things.

1. Make a Day Book. Use five sheets of paper. Write the names of the school days at the tops of the pages: **Monday**, **Tuesday**, **Wednesday**, **Thursday**, **Friday**. Put the pages together. Write something every day. Tell what you did. Tell what other things happened. You may draw pictures to go with your words.

2. Pick the time of year you like best. Draw a picture of it. Show the picture to the class. Have them guess the time of year. Tell the class three things you do then and why you like this time of year.

Mrs. Sing had Grace go to the store. They needed some food for dinner that night. Grace put on her coat and went outside. Then she met her friend Dan. They walked together. Grace got to the store. She found the things she needed. But she could not take them with her. She had left the money at home.

What happened first?

A. Grace met Dan.
B. Grace left the store.
C. Mrs. Sing had Grace go to the store.

Sam and Nat went to work for the first time today. They met when the sun came up. First, they put leaves in big bags. Next, Sam cut the grass. Then Nat cleaned up after him. The two boys worked well together. They made money too!

What happened first?

A. Sam cut the grass.

B. Sam and Nat went to work.

C. Sam and Nat made money.

Ann put the fish in the pan. Then Ron set the table. They were making dinner to surprise Mrs. Bell. She was surprised, all right! She came home with food for dinner for all three of them!

What happened first?

A. Ann put the fish in the pan.
B. Mrs. Bell came home with dinner.
C. Ron set the table.

Snow fell all night. Maria and Carlos were glad. They put on winter coats and went outside. They pushed the snow into big balls for a snowman. Together, they could just pick up the big balls. They made the snowman near the steps. The snowman lasted for three days, watching everyone go by.

What happened first?

A. The snowman lasted for three days.
B. Maria and Carlos put on winter coats.
C. It snowed all night.

Lee's bike didn't work. Lee could not ride it, and she didn't know how to fix it. But Mr. Snow would know how. Mr. Snow lived next door to Lee. A long time ago, he had worked in a bike store. Now Mr. Snow worked on Lee's bike. He showed Lee how to fix it. Then they went bike riding together.

What happened first?

A. Lee and Mr. Snow went bike riding.

B. Lee's bike didn't work.

C. Mr. Snow fixed Lee's bike.

Jack took off old paint all morning. He was helping his mother paint the house. After lunch, he opened a can of red paint. He mixed it. Then he painted the back door. He got some paint on the window. He got some paint on his nose, too. His mom laughed. "You are doing just fine," she said.

What happened first?

A. Jack painted the door.

B. Jack got paint on his nose.

C. Jack took off old paint.

A. Exercising Your Skill

Do you know the games below? Talk about them with classmates. Then decide which step comes first in each game.

Dodge Ball: You are hit by the ball.
The ball comes at you.
You are out.

Jacks: You pick up one jack.
You bounce the ball.
You pick up two jacks.

Tag: You run away.
You are tagged.
Now, you are it.

Simon Says: You move without Simon telling you to.
Simon says what to do.
You do what Simon says.

B. Expanding Your Skill

Pick another game. Tell what happens, in order. (Some games are **Pick Up Sticks**, **Mother**, **May I?**, or **Pin the Tail on the Donkey**.)

C. Exploring Language

Some games have special words that go with them. Look at the game words in the box. Then copy kinds of games on your paper. Write the game words under the games they go with. Add one more game word for each kind of game.

Home run!	You are IT!
Here I come, ready or not!	Jump shot!

ball games	running games

D. Expressing Yourself

Do one of these things.

1. Complete this jump rope chant: "Willie went on a wee trip. What did Willie see?"

   Say the numbers in order. Use numbers and words that begin with the same sound. (One wiggly worm, two tiny tin trumpets, and so on...)

2. Make up a game. Tell your friends what the rules are. Play the game with your friends.

Karen and Jane are good friends. They went to the zoo one day. First, they went to the animal show. There they saw a big snake. Jane would not get close to it. Then they went to see the lions. After that, they went to the snake house. Jane still would not go near the snakes.

What happened first?

A. Karen and Jane went to see the lions.

B. Karen and Jane went to the snake house.

C. Karen and Jane went to the animal show.

Rita liked to make popcorn. Sometimes she made too much. One night she made a lot of popcorn. She gave some to her mother, some to her father, and some to each of her brothers. Everyone ate the popcorn. Her mother smiled. "We will have to watch TV for days to eat all this!" she said.

What happened first?

A. Rita's family ate the popcorn.
B. Rita made a lot of popcorn.
C. Rita gave popcorn to her family.

Pat and her mom had lunch in the city. Then they went to buy new coats. There were many stores in the city. Mom got a blue coat. Pat saw a yellow coat with dots on it. She wanted to get the coat, but her mom said, "It doesn't look good." At last, Pat got a blue coat, too. Then Pat and her mom went home, tired but happy.

What happened first?

A. Pat and her mother went home.

B. Pat and her mother got new coats.

C. Pat and her mother had lunch.

Ben did not like his new glasses. One day, he did not take them to school. He could not read without them. He could not even see his teacher. Everyone and everything looked cloudy. Then Ben wished that he had his glasses. Sue said she liked Ben's glasses. From then on, Ben always had his glasses on.

What happened first?

A. Ben did not take his glasses to school.
B. Everything looked cloudy to Ben.
C. Ben wished he had his glasses.

Ted and his mother went out with a ball and a bat. Ted liked to go after the ball. Ted's mom hit the ball far away. It went over a little hill. Ted looked for the ball. He could not find it. Then Ruff, Ted's dog, ran up to him. Ruff had the ball in his mouth. "You can play ball with us, Ruff," said Ted.

What happened first?

A. Ted and his mother went out to play ball.

B. The ball went over a hill.

C. Ruff ran up to Ted.

Tom walked outside to go to the store. He saw a show all up and down the street. First, he went by a clown doing tricks. Next, he saw boys and girls dancing. Then he walked by a woman who was painting faces. Tom got to the store, but he did not go in. There was so much to see and do outside. Tom turned around and walked back down the street.

What happened first?

A. Tom walked back down the street.
B. Tom saw a street show.
C. Tom got to the store.

Jim and his friends got to school first thing in the morning. They were getting a new teacher. The boys and girls went inside. Then they met Mr. Green. First, Mr. Green gave the children lots of books to read. Jim and the others worked a long time. Then Mr. Green did some funny tricks for them. Everyone liked Mr. Green.

What happened first?

A. Mr. Green did some tricks.
B. The boys and girls went inside the school.
C. Jim and the others worked a long time.

A. Exercising Your Skill

You know how to do many things. Can you tell how to do a thing in order? Read the steps for the jobs below. Tell the step that comes <u>first</u>. Then tell what comes <u>next</u>, and what comes <u>last</u>.

To pour a glass of milk—
>   Open the milk.
>   Get out the milk and a glass.
>   Pour some milk into the glass.

To call a friend—
>   Look up the number.
>   Say hello.
>   Dial the phone.

To clean your teeth—
>   Run water over the brush to clean it off.
>   Put some paste on the brush.
>   Brush your teeth.

B. Expanding Your Skill

Work with a classmate. Pick a job you both can do. Think of all the steps in the job.

Then show everyone how to do it. Draw a picture for each step. Put the pictures in a row. Put them in the right order. Write the name of the job on the first picture. Start with the words, "How to _____ ."

C. Exploring Language

People go through steps in growing up. Read the steps below. Then copy them in order on your paper. Draw a picture to go with each step.

1. a two-year-old child
2. a student in first grade
3. a grown-up

Now look at the sentences in the box. Tell which person above would probably say each sentence.

> I can feed myself now.
> I can take care of children.
> I can read words now.

D. Expressing Yourself

Do one of these things.

1. Bring pictures of yourself to class. They should show how you looked at different times when you were younger. Tell what you could do when you were at the age each picture shows.

2. Make a list of things you can do now that you could not do three or four years ago.

Mrs. Hill wanted to grow some food. She worked a long time outside. She planted seeds. She wanted to grow lots of good things to eat. After many days, plants came up out of the ground. The plants grew very tall. Juan and Monica helped pick the food when it was ready. Then they ate lots of good food for dinner. It was great.

What happened first?

A. Juan and Monica helped pick the food.

B. Everyone ate dinner.

C. Mrs. Hill planted seeds.

Gil took his pet pig, Minnie, to the animal show. Gil wanted Minnie to be in the show. First, all the pigs were put into one place. Next, all the people looked at the pigs. Then some of the people picked the best pig. Minnie was not the best pig, but Gil was not sad. Minnie was named the cleanest pig at the show!

What happened first?

A. Gil took his pig to the show.

B. Minnie was named the cleanest pig.

C. Some people picked the best pig.

Sandy got her bat. She was ready. She had to hit the ball far. She and her friends wanted to win the game. The ball came at her. Sandy hit it. The ball went a long way. It landed out on the grass. Then Sandy ran as fast as she could go. She made it all the way around. It was a home run!

What happened first?

A. Sandy hit a home run.

B. The ball came at Sandy.

C. Sandy ran as fast as she could.

Dan wanted to surprise Jill. He got some bird seed. Then he and Jill went to the park. Dan gave food to the birds there every day. The birds always came very close. Dan wanted Jill to see. But today the birds did not come close. They all went up into a tree. Then Jill saw why. The birds still liked Dan. But they did not like the cat that had come with him!

What happened first?

A. Dan and Jill went to the park.

B. The birds did not come close.

C. Dan got some bird seed.

After Mr. Willis pushed up the window, a bee came in.
Jackie saw it first. She yelled. Next, Luis put his coat over
his head. Then Sam hid under a table. Rita stayed very still
so the bee would not bite her. No one was doing school
work any more. The bee made a sound. Then it went back
outside. Maybe it did not like school.

What happened first?

A. Mr. Willis pushed up the window.

B. The bee made a sound and went outside.

C. Luis put his coat over his head.

Max and Tim had no money. They went to the pet store for fun. They looked at the animals for a long time. Then Mr. Jakes asked if they wanted to help. Max and Tim gave food to the dogs. The boys petted the dogs and played with them. They had fun, and they made some money too.

What happened first?

A. Max and Tim looked at all the animals.

B. Max and Tim gave food to the dogs.

C. Max and Tim made money.

A. Exercising Your Skill

Pretend you are writing a letter to a friend. Answer these questions by telling which thing you would do **first**.

1. write the letter

   (or)

   put the letter in an envelope?

2. put the stamp on

   (or)

   lick it?

3. put the address on

   (or)

   put the letter into a mailbox?

B. Expanding Your Skill

Think of all the steps in writing and mailing a letter. Draw a picture for each step on separate pieces of paper. Mix up the sheets. See if your classmates can put the steps in order.

C. Exploring Language

Make a post card to tell a friend about a trip you once took or would like to take. On one side of a sheet of paper, draw a picture of the place. On the other side of the paper, draw a line down the middle. To the left of the line, tell your friend about your trip. To the right of the line, put your friend's address.

D. Expressing Yourself

Do one of these things.

1. What do you do to get ready for a trip? Tell what you would do first, second, and third, before you leave for a trip.

2. Play "I'm Going on a Trip" with a group of other students. Sit in a circle. Pick someone to go first. The first person says, "I'm going on a trip, and I'm taking _____ ." The person picks something to finish the sentence. Then the second person says the same sentence, adds one new thing, and repeats the first thing. The third person adds a new thing and repeats the first two things in order. And so on.